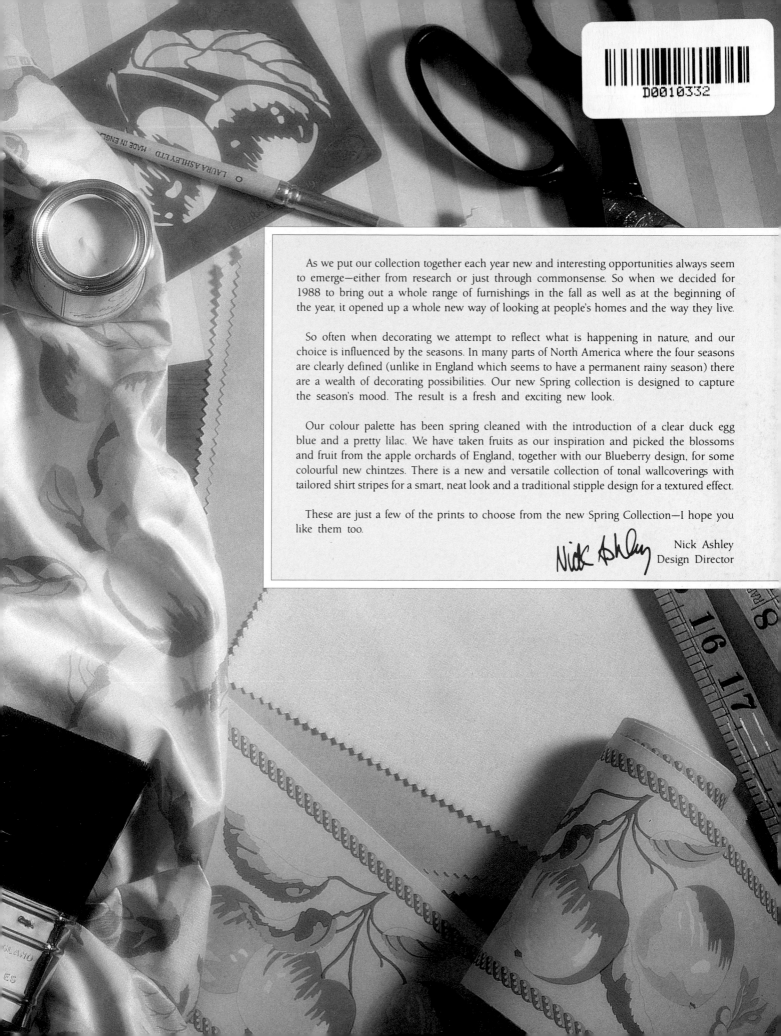

As we put our collection together each year new and interesting opportunities always seem to emerge—either from research or just through commonsense. So when we decided for 1988 to bring out a whole range of furnishings in the fall as well as at the beginning of the year, it opened up a whole new way of looking at people's homes and the way they live.

So often when decorating we attempt to reflect what is happening in nature, and our choice is influenced by the seasons. In many parts of North America where the four seasons are clearly defined (unlike in England which seems to have a permanent rainy season) there are a wealth of decorating possibilities. Our new Spring collection is designed to capture the season's mood. The result is a fresh and exciting new look.

Our colour palette has been spring cleaned with the introduction of a clear duck egg blue and a pretty lilac. We have taken fruits as our inspiration and picked the blossoms and fruit from the apple orchards of England, together with our Blueberry design, for some colourful new chintzes. There is a new and versatile collection of tonal wallcoverings with tailored shirt stripes for a smart, neat look and a traditional stipple design for a textured effect.

These are just a few of the prints to choose from the new Spring Collection—I hope you like them too.

Nick Ashley
Design Director

BLUEBERRY
DUCK EGG

A bedroom like a piece of summer sky at the top of a grand old house in Hampshire. Outside, the house is knee-deep in old-fashioned flowers. Inside, white and duck egg blue give the room its sense of innocence and pale sunshine. Breezy curtains made up in Blueberry chintz are caught back high up to show off the bonnet-shaped window bays. Here the berries in crushed strawberry look beautifully ripe against the cool blue. Laurel Berries, in country furnishing cotton is a simpler pattern of scattered laurel sprigs. Rich red berries and translucent leaves outlined against a hazy blue English sky. It is as if a warm morning sun has steeped the colours in a clear, fresh light to remind us of summer.

Light streaming through glazed chintz enriches its colour, making it a wonderful fabric for curtains.

BLUEBERRY BORDER

LYME REGIS

LAUREL BERRIES

BLUEBERRY

EMERALD

JADE

CRUSHED STRAWBERRY

SCARLET

CLUB CHECK

DUCK EGG

ORCHARD
D U C K   E G G

This tiny, secret garden comes straight off the dining-room of a converted London mews house, and in summer the doors are flung open and meals taken al fresco. Then, the natural greenery is set off by new duck egg blue, green-tinged with the summery freshness of clear water. The delicacy of wrought iron furniture is brought out by the pale prettiness of the new Orchard chintz, with its pattern of apples dappled in shades of apricot on a duck egg ground. Fruit has always been a particularly appropriate motif for the dining-room, but never more so than in this outdoor setting.

A delicate water-colour palette brings a sense of light and airiness to the dining room—the natural colours of the Lyme Regis vinyl wall-covering in stone on white and the pastel shades of the Orchard chintz.

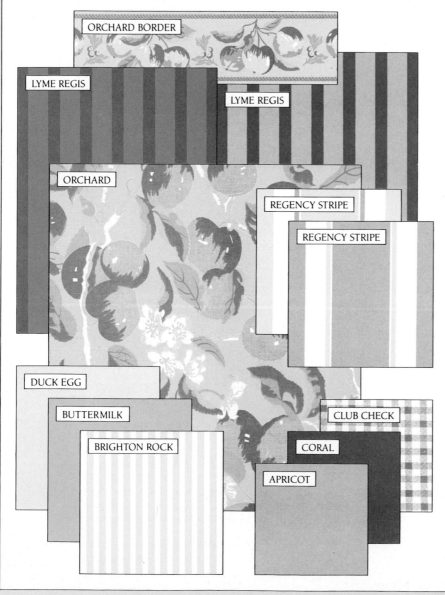

ORCHARD BORDER

LYME REGIS

LYME REGIS

ORCHARD

REGENCY STRIPE

REGENCY STRIPE

DUCK EGG

BUTTERMILK

CLUB CHECK

BRIGHTON ROCK

CORAL

APRICOT

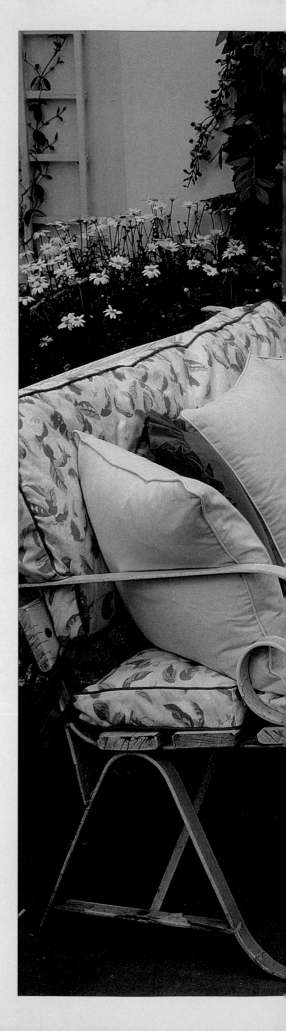

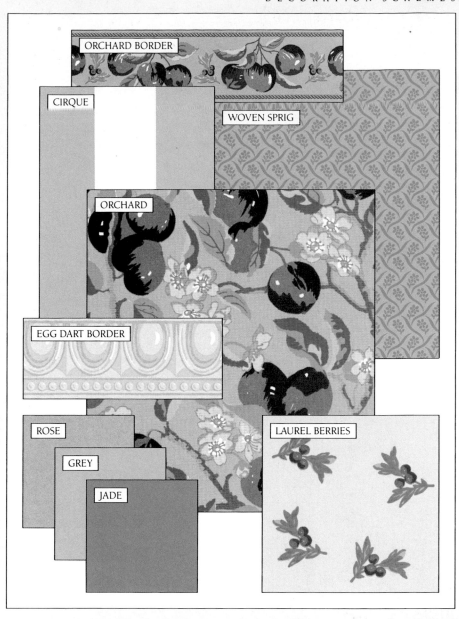

ORCHARD BORDER

CIRQUE

WOVEN SPRIG

ORCHARD

EGG DART BORDER

ROSE

GREY

JADE

LAUREL BERRIES

ORCHARD
G R E Y

The living room, situated at the top of this old mill house, takes advantage of sweeping views across country. Flooded with light from four windows its grey and white colour scheme reflects the pure silvery quality of our Northern daylight. Chintz curtains in the new Orchard print add warm tones to complete this sophisticated combination of colours.

Pale pink, crimson-splashed peonies with a burst of long, cool green leaves against the grey and white-striped Cirque wallcovering perfectly mirror the colours of the Orchard chintz.

The striking effect of rich colours and shades of light on a profusion of apples. Fruit has always been used in the decorative arts: the exuberance and variety it brings to decoration appeals to artists and designers alike.

ST. CLEMENTS BORDER

ORANGES

LEMONS

ST. CLEMENTS

LYME REGIS

INFINITY

FIRENZE

SAGE

CORAL

JADE

CLUB CHECK

BUTTERMILK

SMOKE

ST. CLEMENTS
SAGE

Oranges and lemons say the bells of St. Clements. This print tells a story of ripe fruit warmed by a hot harvest sun and captured for many seasons to come on a beautifully mellow linen union fabric.

St. Clements, a pattern of tumbling leafy oranges and lemons in linen union is used for the curtains and valance, while the cushions on the Windsor carver's chair are in Oranges country furnishing cotton. The freshness of the Lemons print enlivens the vinyl wallcovering.

Fruit prints, with their sunburnt colours, recall the farm business of harvesting, and at the same time, the traditional task of preserve-making with its garnet-coloured jellies and baskets of oranges and lemons waiting to be made into marmalade.

PAPRIKA
WHITE

This sparklingly bright and cheerful bathroom in a Scottish country house is decorated with the vivacious new peasant prints. It is an old-fashioned bathroom with a fireplace, modified to accomodate an antique brass towel-rail on which two new Windsor Rose towels are kept well-warmed. Tania, a new vinyl wallcovering, sets the tone with a lively print of scarlet flowers framed in blue lattice.

Paprika is the keynote of the new peasant prints, positively dancing with small, stylized wild flowers, here in sunny tones of scarlet, emerald, blue and golden yellow.

The tablecloth and made to measure Roman blind add a comforting note of scarlet with soft tones of emerald, grey and blue in a naive print, Pinafore.

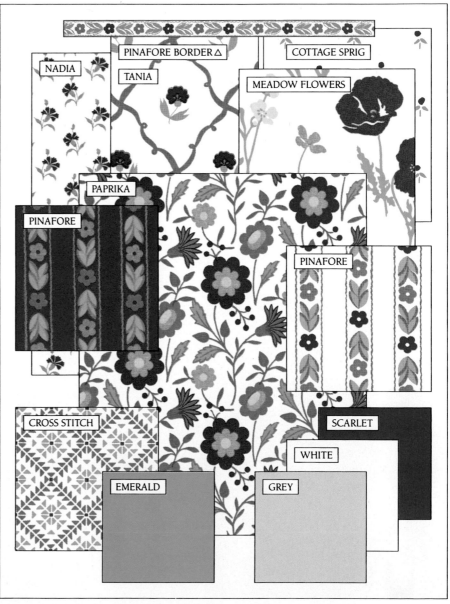

PINAFORE BORDER △

NADIA

TANIA

COTTAGE SPRIG

MEADOW FLOWERS

PAPRIKA

PINAFORE

PINAFORE

CROSS STITCH

SCARLET

WHITE

EMERALD

GREY

LOUISE
APRICOT

This elegant drawing room of a colonial style house evokes equally an air of formality and comfort. The main reception room of the house, it is also a place to relax with a good book or to write letters at the small mahogany bureau tucked in between the windows.

The sense of a period interior is created by the pair of sash windows, the period portraits and the solid pieces of mahogany furniture placed deliberately around the edges of the room. Dominating the center of the room is an inviting love seat, covered in one of the prettiest new country furnishing cotton fabrics, Louise. Its perfect posies of pale apricot pansies with aquamarine and jade leaves lend a lightness and softness to the darker furniture. The same print is used for the curtains which are hung simply from wooden poles in keeping with the style of the room.

The posies from the Louise print are repeated on the wallpaper border which runs around the top of the room. Its companion vinyl wallcovering, Louise Stripe—an apricot and aquamarine stripe on a background of tiny aquamarine stars—gives the room its smart air and acts as a perfect foil for the dark portraits. As a country furnishing cotton used on the Somerville upholstered armchair, Louise Stripe emphasises the mix of stripes and posies that create a refreshingly elegant room.

LOUISE
L I L A C

Tucked in under a lofty gable end, this bedroom's demure country air is tempered by a country house elegance. The new Louise print, used for the curtains and comforter, perfectly captures this mood of simple but smart.

The new colour theme, lilac, has a gentle sweetness that is particularly suited to evoke the serene calm of a country bedroom. The Infinity vinyl wallcovering is hardly more than a stippling of lilac like the spots on a speckled egg, with a pretty border of posies above to link with the curtains. Lots of fresh white paintwork and a stencilled chest of drawers add to the dreamy lightness of the room.

Louise Stripe is a companion print for Louise; a jade, lilac and rose stripe, on a background of tiny lilac stars. It provides a preamble to the main colour theme.

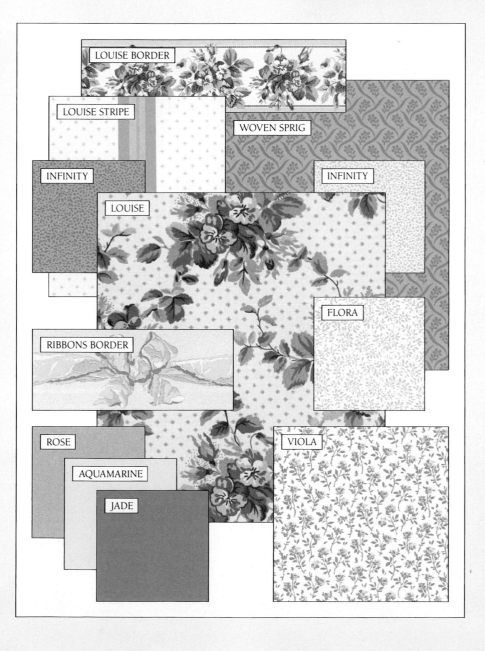

LOUISE BORDER

LOUISE STRIPE

WOVEN SPRIG

INFINITY

INFINITY

LOUISE

FLORA

RIBBONS BORDER

ROSE

VIOLA

AQUAMARINE

JADE

A close up of the curtains shows the prettiness of Louise's meandering sprays of sweet pansies and rose-tinted buds.

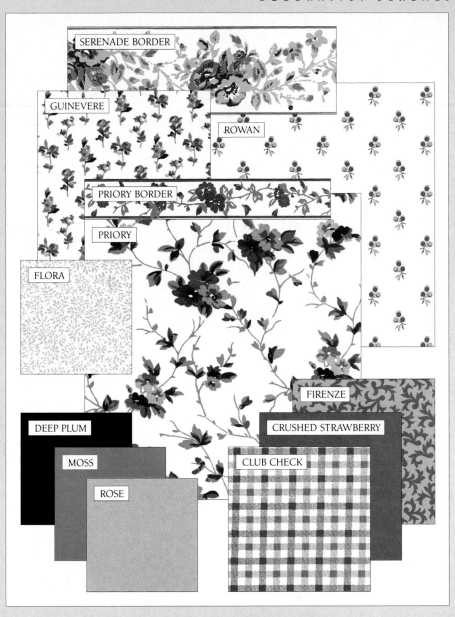

SERENADE BORDER

GUINEVERE

ROWAN

PRIORY BORDER

PRIORY

FLORA

FIRENZE

DEEP PLUM

CRUSHED STRAWBERRY

MOSS

CLUB CHECK

ROSE

PRIORY
C R U S H E D S T R A W B E R R Y

The owner of this house, a city dweller, with dreams of a rural way of life, chose a profusion of wild flowers in truly rustic style to transform this urban dining room into an idyllic country haven. The crisp colours of lilac, crushed strawberry and moss in the Priory design on vinyl wallcovering and curtains are perfectly set off by sturdy beams and lots of polished antique wood. This make-believe is continued by squab chair cushions in the pretty co-ordinate print, Guinevere, and Star Patchwork cushions on the sunny window seats. Half-shutters hide the view of the street outside, and the daylight is softened by delicate Posies lace.

Cushions by the window bring together all the prints in the room; and the window seat, covered in our new ottoman fabric, picks out the unifying colour theme.

CHARLESTON GRAPES
G R E Y

The thoroughly contemporary feel of Charleston Grapes is right for this studio in modernist mood. A photographer lives and works here, in a characterful area of East London known as Shoreditch where the battered Victorian and Georgian workshops are being revitalized as studios for photographers, fashion designers and film companies.

Refreshing citrus lemon against cooling grey makes a city palette that tones perfectly with acres of varnished wood floor and attenuated metal furniture. The sofa is upholstered in bold and splashy, but light Charleston Grapes in linen union. Walls are covered in the most minimal of vinyl wallcovering, pale-grey Infinity; and the buttermilk chintz blinds and ottoman seat cushions on the campaign chairs blend effortlessly into the unruffled mood.

On the floor, a Bloomsbury rug, designed in the Thirties by Vanessa Bell for Virginia Woolf, has the spare geometrical charm of abstract shape and muted colour. Hand-woven in Yorkshire from pure wool.

A second sofa is upholstered in new grey ottoman fabric, whose lines of cording add more surface interest against the grains of linen union. A buttermilk cushion constrasts with the glazed sheen of chintz.

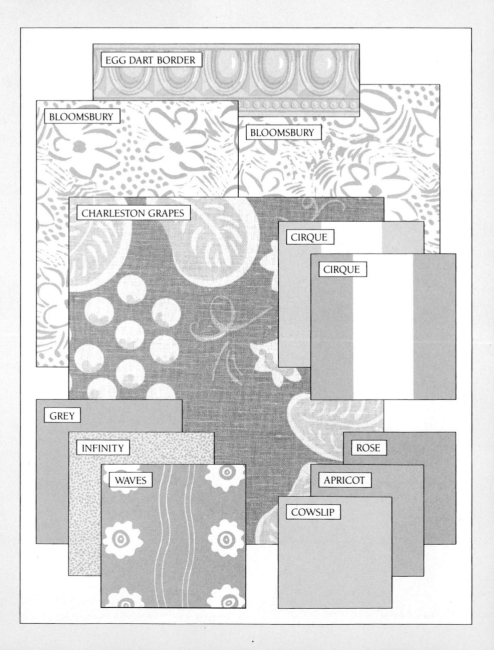

EGG DART BORDER

BLOOMSBURY

BLOOMSBURY

CHARLESTON GRAPES

CIRQUE

CIRQUE

GREY

INFINITY

WAVES

ROSE

APRICOT

COWSLIP

ACANTHUS
SMOKE

The hall is too often an opportunity for decoration missed. Yet it is an extremely important part of a house, the room onto which all the others give. A cool, understated colour scheme like this one of smoke, ivory and plum is a contrast to main rooms of livelier colour and pattern and it is a pleasure to dive into the shady depths of the hall after basking in a sunny drawing-room.

At the same time, a corner such as this one in the corridor of an Old Hall in Staffordshire can become an inviting niche in its own right, a perfect place to take tea or curl up with a good book. Its window is dressed with lavishly-printed curtains in our new Acanthus linen union. An intricate pattern of stylized leaves and flowerheads in subtle tones of smoke and plum, this is an original design in the tradition of seventeenth century worsted fabrics or tapestries.

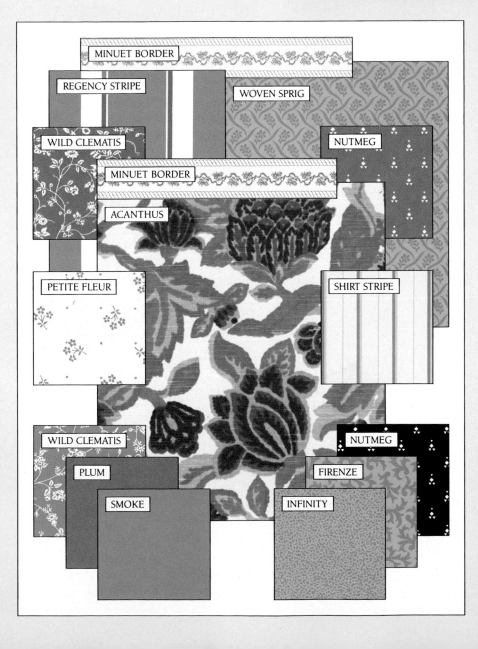

MINUET BORDER

REGENCY STRIPE

WOVEN SPRIG

WILD CLEMATIS

NUTMEG

MINUET BORDER

ACANTHUS

PETITE FLEUR

SHIRT STRIPE

WILD CLEMATIS

NUTMEG

PLUM

FIRENZE

SMOKE

INFINITY

Woven Sprig is one of the most versatile of the new vinyl wallcoverings; simple enough for a cottage, smart enough for the town. Its broken weave pattern is a light alternative to more definite stripes or checks. Against it, new Acanthus-printed linen union has a pleasantly textured tapestry feel.

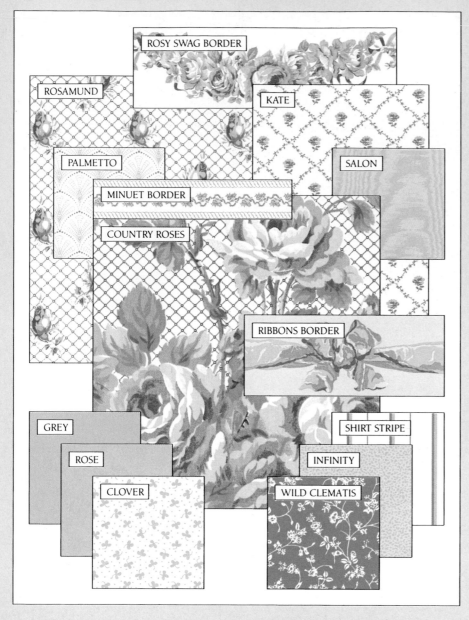

ROSY SWAG BORDER

ROSAMUND

KATE

PALMETTO

SALON

MINUET BORDER

COUNTRY ROSES

RIBBONS BORDER

GREY

SHIRT STRIPE

ROSE

INFINITY

CLOVER

WILD CLEMATIS

COUNTRY ROSES
R O S E

The country charm of a roomful of English roses in soft tones of pink and moss on white is captured on this Victorian design, Country Roses. Here, on comforter, pillowshams and decorative pillows it co-ordinates perfectly with our rose and white striped sheets, pillowcases and dust ruffle trimmed in a pretty floral swagged border.

Country Roses, a print of English cabbage roses, is particularly suitable for a bedroom. It may also be used to great effect in more formal rooms to proclaim one of nature's most precious colours, rose.

To compliment this bed ensemble select a co-ordinating piece of furniture from our upholstered furniture collection which includes sofas, loveseats, chaises, chairs and ottomans.

LOUISE BORDER

TRACERY

MORNING TRACERY

PETRA

FIRENZE

ALBA ROSES

WOVEN SPRIG

RIBBONS BORDER

LYME REGIS

CLUB CHECK

COWSLIP

KATE

JADE

ALBA ROSES
J A D E

The versatility of the cowslip yellow is shown in this small sitting room in which the green of the garden outside is echoed by the pale yellow and green of the furnishings.

A simple chair is made to look quite inviting with a loose cover in Club Check in jade and cowslip, and a co-ordinating cushion in Morning Tracery.

Here the master print Alba Roses in chintz, used in the cowslip and jade colourway on the curtains, is combined with the Lyme Regis wallcovering in cowslip and the classic Rosy Swag border.

On the chintz covered sofa in Alba Roses lie cushions in the co-ordinating Club Check prints.

SHELLS
SAPPHIRE

The owner of this pretty seaside house wanted a truly traditional bathroom complete with enormous bath and antique towel rail, and chose the time-honoured combination of sapphire and white. The seaside theme is brought indoors with the Shells tiles and matching shoreline border tiles in colours of sea and sky. Vinyl wallcovering in Bembridge and drapes in Regatta make for a pretty mixture of prints brought together by the sapphire colour scheme. Natural sponges, model ships, striped towels, and the room's fresh cleanliness create an atmosphere redolent of life in a seafront town.

A neatly folded pile of co-ordinating towels in Regency stripe and a Windsor Rose jacquard design provides real old-fashioned comfort. The Shells motif on the tiles was originally found on a Regency wallpaper border.

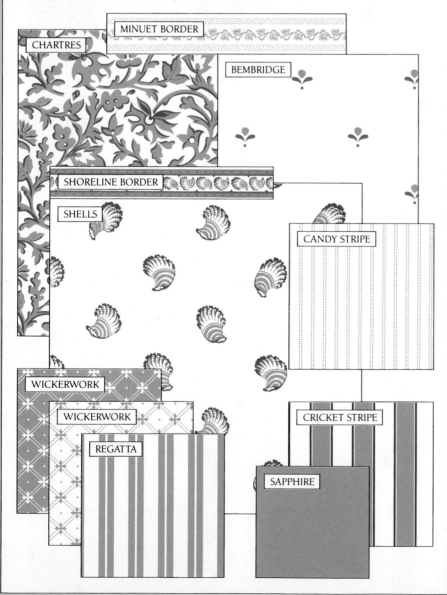

CHARTRES

MINUET BORDER

BEMBRIDGE

SHORELINE BORDER

SHELLS

CANDY STRIPE

WICKERWORK

WICKERWORK

CRICKET STRIPE

REGATTA

SAPPHIRE

BEDLINEN
100% COTTON

Laura Ashley's elegant 100% cotton bedlinens are available exclusively at Laura Ashley shops throughout the United States, Canada, and Laura Ashley by Post. Sheets and pillowcases are made of luxurious 200 count cotton percale with an easy-care *no iron* finish. Co-ordinating accessories, including comforters, shams, bed ruffles, duvets and decorative pillows, are available in 200 count 50% cotton/50% polyester.

Emma (*shown below, Ref. 517415*) in subtle pastel shades of rose, apricot, aquamarine and sapphire fills a bedroom with a light country freshness.

Ticking Stripe (*shown at right, Ref. 039072*), a simple stripe in sapphire on white is complemented by a classic floral border.

Cranford (*shown on page 32, Ref. 379229*) is Laura Ashley's newest pattern in an elegant floral of smoke and rose on a stone ground.

FLAT SHEETS

	Code	Price
Twin	648	36.00
Full	650	48.00
Queen	652	60.00
King	654	72.00

FITTED SHEETS

Twin	649	36.00
Full	651	48.00
Queen	653	60.00
King	655	72.00

PILLOWCASES

Standard (pair)	646	44.00
King (pair)	647	52.00

PILLOW SHAMS

Standard	691	60.00
King	692	72.00

COMFORTERS

Twin	657	155.00
Full	658	195.00
Queen	659	240.00
King	660	275.00

BED RUFFLES

Twin	663	96.00
Full	664	110.00
Queen	665	120.00
King	666	130.00

DUVETS

Twin	667	140.00
Full	668	160.00
Queen	669	180.00
King	639	200.00

DECORATIVE PILLOWS

Breakfast	636	50.00
Square*	633	50.00
Round**	634	50.00
Neckroll***	635	50.00

*Cranford and Ticking Stripe only.
**Emma and Cranford only.
***Emma and Ticking Stripe only.

BEDLINEN
B R I D A L   L A C E

Bridal lace (*shown below, Ref. 020100*), is Heirloom quality; the quintessence of luxury and romantic indulgence in the purest white trimmed with an elaborate border of ruffled lace. In a luxurious 200 thread count of easy care 50% cotton, 50% polyester, Bridal lace sheets and accessories combine with other Laura Ashley designs to create a personalized bedroom decor. Available in selected shops and through Laura Ashley by Post.

For Cranford (*shown at left*) see page 30.

FLAT SHEETS	Code	Price
Twin	648	24.00
Full	650	32.00
Queen	652	40.00
King	654	48.00

FITTED SHEETS		
Twin	649	18.00
Full	651	22.00
Queen	653	32.00
King	655	40.00

PILLOWCASES		
Standard (pair)	646	32.00
King (pair)	647	36.00

PILLOW SHAMS		
Standard	691	50.00
King	692	60.00

COMFORTERS		
Twin	657	145.00
Full	658	175.00
Queen	659	210.00
King	660	250.00

BED RUFFLES		
Twin	663	85.00
Full	664	95.00
Queen	665	110.00
King	666	120.00

DECORATIVE PILLOWS		
Square	633	40.00
Round	634	40.00
Neckroll	635	40.00

BEDLINEN

ALBA ROSES & COUNTRY LATTICE

Alba Roses (*shown below, Ref. 484136*) is a sunny romance in a traditional chintz floral and companion club check in cowslip yellow and smoke. In a luxurious 200 thread count of 50% cotton/50% polyester.

Country Lattice (*shown at right, Ref. 476144*) evokes country innocence. Charming rose coloured posies on a sapphire lattice background co-ordinate with a print of posie clusters on white. In a luxurious 200 thread count of 50% cotton/50% polyester.

FITTED SHEETS

Twin	649	20.00
Full	651	28.00
Queen	653	37.00
King	655	44.00

PILLOWCASES

Standard (pair)	646	30.00
King (pair)	647	35.00

PILLOW SHAMS

Standard	691	44.00
King	692	55.00

COMFORTERS

Twin	657	125.00
Full	658	160.00
Queen	659	185.00
King	660	220.00

BED RUFFLES

Twin	663	68.00
Full	664	78.00
Queen	665	88.00
King	666	98.00

DUVETS

Twin	667	75.00
Full	668	90.00
Queen	669	100.00
King	639	125.00

FLAT SHEETS

	Code	Price
Twin	648	20.00
Full	650	28.00
Queen	652	37.00
King	654	44.00

DECORATIVE PILLOWS

Square	633	37.50
Round (Alba Roses only)	634	37.50
Neckroll	635	37.50
Breakfast (Country Lattice only)	636	37.50

LACE
BY THE YARD

Use Laura Ashley lace by the yard to dress your home in Victorian style, including curtains, tablecloths and decorating accessories. Produced on original nineteenth century Jacquard looms in both 8 point and 12 point Nottingham lace. In delicate designs of floral swags, they are available in White and Ivory.

Also available in the Laura Ashley Lace Collection are Nottingham lace bedspreads and lace panels with tie-backs. Lace: 95% cotton, 5% polyester. Hand or machine washable (40ºC) cool iron.

To order, call toll free 24 hours a day 1-800-367-2000.

CHINA & LACE
ALICE CHINA

The classic English table setting featuring a complete collection of our Alice China which can be used for breakfast, lunch, tea or dinner. Each item comes beautifully gift boxed and is microwave safe. Product Code: 883.

Tea for Two Set*	434640	100.00
Large Jug	999662	40.00
Cache Pot	999639	45.00
Teapot	999641	50.00
Mugs (set of 2)	999632	25.00
Candlesticks (each)	434546	24.00
Teacups and Saucers (set of 4)	999633	75.00
Teaplates (set of 4)	999645	45.00
Sugar and Creamer	999656	40.00
10″ Dinner Plates (set of 4)	434647	72.00
Soup Plates (set of 4)	434648	72.00
Salad Bowl	434651	60.00
Oval Meat Dish	434654	60.00
Coffee Pot	434642	65.00
Demitasse Cups & Saucers (set of 4)	434544	45.00
Egg Cups (set of 4)	434545	24.00

*Tea for Two Set includes 2 teacups and saucers, 2 teaplates, sugar bowl, creamer and teapot.

LACE DINING COLLECTION

Our collection of Nottingham lace tablecloths, napkins and placemats are woven on traditional Jacquard looms that have been producing lace since the Nineteenth Century. The design is a delicate one of floral swags, ribbons and bows on a fine 8 point lace. Made from 95% cotton and 5% polyester. Available in White (020100) or Ivory (020763).

Tablecloths	Size	Code	Price
Rectangular	70 x 88 in	530	85.00
Round	68 in diam	494	75.00
Square	54 x 54 in	451	65.00
Napkins (set of 4)	19 x 19 in	452	35.00
Placemats (set of 4)	16 x 11 in	507	25.00

MADE TO ORDER
BEDCOVERINGS AND WINDOW TREATMENTS

Laura Ashley is a specialist in producing Made to Measure curtains, blinds, valances and bedcoverings. This professional service offers a selection of beautifully hand-finished products in a wide choice of designs on natural fabrics. Each item is individually made to your specific measurements; the emphasis is on quality, craftsmanship and attention to detail.

Choose from a wide assortment of window treatments including traditional Triple Pleat curtains, Pencil Pleat curtains, Frilled curtains, Bullion trim curtains or Festoon and Roman blinds. Or, select a custom made down or polyester comforter, bedspread or coverlet, bed ruffles, pillow shams, duvet covers and tablerounds. All are available from any print or colourway of country furnishing cotton, drawing room fabric, chintz or linen union.

MADE TO ORDER
L A C E

Laura Ashley lace curtains are made from 8 point Nottingham lace produced on original nineteenth century Jacquard looms. In a delicate design of ribbons, flowers and bows with decorative scalloped edges at either side, the curtains are available in White or Ivory. Made to your own choice of length, lace curtains are available in a selection of widths.

For beautifully different effects, you may choose to use a single curtain flat as a panel, or have a single gathered curtain, or a pair of gathered curtains. Highly versatile, they should be used with hooks and a rod.

Open or drawn, Laura Ashley lace curtains will look beautiful both with or without main curtains.

For custom orders, call 1-800-223-6917 and ask for Special Orders Dept.

CUSHIONS

This year our cushion collection offers a wide and versatile choice of fabrics, designs and colourways to add that finishing touch to any room. There are deeper frills on the round and square frilled cushion covers, and the round frilled is larger and more luxurious.

All cushion covers are made from pure cotton apart from the square piped linen union cushion cover which is 60% linen and 40% cotton. Covers may be purchased either separately or with soft feather cushion pads of the highest quality.

Bottom row from left to right:

1. Round frilled cover in CFC PAPRIKA K186 Multi White	397 672242
2. Square piped cover in Chintz SAPPHIRE	525 020107
3. Round frilled cover in CFC POLYANTHUS K88 Sapphire Multi White	397 494137
4. Square piped cover in Chintz COWSLIP	525 020522
5. Square piped cover in CFC CLUBCHECK E34 Cowslip/Jade/White	511 592432
6. Round frilled cover in CFC COUNTRY LATTICE K107 Cowslip Multi White	397 020425

Top row from left to right:

1. Round frilled cover in CFC CAMPION R143 White/Sapphire	397 021073
2. Star Patchwork Sapphire/Cowslip	482 999677
3. Square frilled cover in CFC MORNING TRACERY F948 Cowslip Multi White	512 478424
4. Square piped cover in Chintz JADE	525 020522

SQUARE PIPED CUSHION COVERS

	Size	Code	Price
Chintz	15 x 15 in	525	30.00
CFC*	15 x 15 in	511	30.00
Linen Union	15 x 15 in	471	30.00
DRF**	15 x 15 in	395	35.00

ROUND FRILLED CUSHION COVERS

CFC*	15 in diam	397	30.00

SQUARE FRILLED CUSHION COVERS

Chintz	15 x 15 in	472	30.00
CFC*	15 x 15 in	512	30.00
DRF**	15 x 15 in	473	35.00

STAR PATCHWORK CUSHION COVERS

CFC*	15 x 15 in	482	35.00

CUSHION PADS

Round Pad	520 513999	12.50
Square Pad	520 512999	12.50

*Country Furnishing Cotton.
**Drawing Room Fabric.

Bottom row from left to right:

1. Round frilled cover in CFC EMMA C17 Multi Apricot/White	397 517415
2. Round frilled cover in CFC KATE F373 Rose/Moss/White	397 173080
3. Square frilled cover in CFC CAMPION R143 White/Rose	512 021067
4. Square piped cover in Chintz ROSE	525 020114
5. Square frilled cover in CFC PRIORY F950 Crushed Strawberry Multi White	512 480426

Top row:

1. Square frilled cover in DRF COUNTRY ROSES F430 Rose Multi White	473 089144
2. Square frilled cover in CFC COUNTRY LATTICE K107 Rose Multi White	512 476144

CERAMIC TILES

8 INCH FLOOR & WALL TILES

The large 8 inch tile (7⅞ x 7⅞) are particularly suitable for walls and floors not subject to heavy wear. Professional advice may be required for application. Available in packs of 25 to cover approximately 10 square feet. Made in Italy on a terracotta biscuit.

	Code	Price
8 in Floor & Wall Tiles	681	5.00*

6 INCH WALL TILES

The 6 x 6 inch wall tiles are available in packs of 22 to cover approximately 5 square feet. Easy to apply, these should be used on walls. Made in Italy on a terracotta biscuit.

	Code	Price
6 in Wall Tiles	686	2.50*

6 x 3 BORDER TILES

The ceramic border tiles are designed for use with the 6 x 6 inch wall tiles. Available in packs of 10, they cover approximately 5 linear feet. Made in Italy on a terracotta biscuit.

	Code	Price
6 x 3 Border Tiles	396	2.00*

6 x 6 IMPERIAL WALL TILES

The 6 x 6 wall tiles are available in packs of 18 to cover approximately half a square yard. These are easy to apply and should be used on walls. Made in the U.K. on a white biscuit.

	Code	Price
6 x 6 Imperial Wall Tiles	606	2.50*

6 x 3 IMPERIAL BORDER TILES

The Imperial border tiles that coordinate with the 6 x 6 Imperial wall tiles are available in packs of 10 and cover approximately 5 linear feet. Made in the U.K. on a white biscuit.

	Code	Price
6 x 3 Imperial Border Tiles	945	2.00*

*per tile.

IMPERIAL WALL TILES 6 in	606
SCARBOROUGH FAIR K276 Rose Multi White	567144
WICKER CORNER K215 Rose/White	566066
IMPERIAL BORDER TILES 6 x 3 in	945
WICKER BORDER K315 Rose/White	526066
FLOOR TILES 8 in	681
WHITE	020110

IMPERIAL WALL TILES 6 in	606
PROVIDENCE K254 Sapphire/Rose/White	568010
WICKER CORNER K251 Sapphire/White	566072
IMPERIAL BORDER TILES 6 x 3 in	945
WICKER BORDER K315 Sapphire/White	526072
FLOOR TILES 8 in	681
SAPPHIRE	020107

IMPERIAL WALL TILES 6 in	606
COUNTRY POSY K108 Rose Multi White	492144
IMPERIAL BORDER TILES 6 x 3 in	945
COUNTRY POSY K302 Rose Multi White	545144

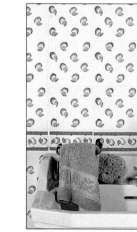

IMPERIAL WALL TILES 6 in	606
SHELLS F840 Sapphire/White	471072
IMPERIAL BORDER TILES 6 x 3 in	945
SHORELINE F841 Sapphire/White	472072

IMPERIAL WALL TILES 6 in	606
ORCHARD K253 Coral/Moss/White	569117
IMPERIAL BORDER TILES 6 x 3 in	945
WICKER BORDER K315 Moss/White	526024
FLOOR TILES 8 in	681
WHITE	020110

WALL TILES 6 in	686
TERRACOTTA	020111
FLOOR TILES 8 in	681
MR. JONES K258 Burgundy/Navy/Sand	564260

TOWELS
WINDSOR ROSE

Understated elegance and luxury in a plush, generously sized solid color towel featuring a distinctive rose border.

Aquamarine	601340
Jade	601339
Sapphire	601107
Smoke	601106
Cream	601110
Cowslip	601522
Sand	601109
Rose	601114
Plum	601112
White	601100

	Size	Code	Price
Bath Towel	52 in x 28 in	622	18.00
Hand Towel	20 in x 32 in	623	12.00
Wash Cloth	13 in x 13 in	624	5.00

REGENCY STRIPE

Distinctive stripes with the added touch of a woven rope piping border and tailored hem.

Sapphire	197258
Aquamarine	197268
Rose	197080

	Size	Code	Price
Bath Towel	50 in x 28 in	622	18.00
Hand Towel	20 in x 32 in	623	.12.00
Wash Cloth	13 in x 13 in	624	5.00

All Laura Ashley towels are made of 100% cotton. Available through Laura Ashley by Post. Not all styles and colours available in all shops.

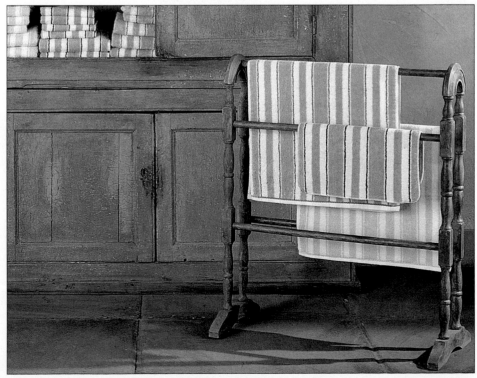

To order, call toll free 24 hours a day 1-800-367-2000.

LIGHTING

Our lighting collection will provide you with a wide choice of beautiful designs and colours to suit any room whatever its size or style. Choose from either hard pleat or shirred shades in a wide variety of patterns. Select from these pages your perfect combination of shade and base.

WOODEN COLUMN BASE

A perfect lamp for home or office available in white with a band of color in rose (020114) or sapphire (020107). It is sold as a set with the lampshade.

GINGER JAR LAMPBASE

The classically shaped table lamp which features a glazed ceramic base in white (020100) or cream (020110) is available in 3 sizes. The perfect base to display a criply pleated shade or a softly shirred shade.

HARD PLEAT LAMPSHADE

Available in 8 print colourways, 2 solids. Fits all ginger jar lampbases.

SHIRRED LAMPSHADE

Available in 11 print colourways. Fits all ginger jar lampbases.

WOODEN COLUMN LAMPBASE AND SHADE
height including fitting: 14 in
Product Code: 570   Price: 70.00

HARD PLEAT LAMPSHADE
SMALL height: 7 in
Product Code: 578   Price: 35.00

MEDIUM height: 11 in
Product Code: 577   Price: 40.00

LARGE height: 11½ in
Product Code: 576   Price: 45.00

SHIRRED LAMPSHADE
SMALL height: 6½ in
Product Code: 583   Price: 40.00

MEDIUM height: 10½ in
Product Code: 585   Price: 50.00

LARGE height: 11 in
Product Code: 587   Price: 55.00

GINGER JAR LAMPBASE
SMALL height from base to top of lamp: 14½ in
Product Code: 575   Price: 45.00

GINGER JAR LAMPBASE
MEDIUM height from base to top of lamp: 21½ in
Product Code: 574   Price: 50.00

GINGER JAR LAMPBASE
LARGE height from base to top of lamp: 24¾ in
Product Code: 573   Price: 60.00

WALLPAPER BORDERS

Our collection of printed paper borders for 1988 includes a versatile new selection of designs and colourways, as shown here and on the catalogue cover. New floral and fruit borders co-ordinate with a wide range of designs; and tonal borders complement our new collection of tonal wallcoverings. Used on a wall, a border can define the space and scale of any room or provide an effective outline for windows, fireplaces and doors.

	Code	Price
Wallpaper Borders	302	$15.00 per pack

Widths:

1 in	two rolls per pack
2¼ in	two rolls per pack
4¼ in	one roll per pack

Length per roll: 11 yards

Shown at top, from left to right:

1. PRIORY BORDER (On Wall)	2¼ in wide	
K282 Sapphire Multi White	533137	
2. SERENADE (On Table)	4¼ in wide	
K30 Sapphire/White	497072	
3. POLKA (On Table)	2¼ in wide	
F46 Mustard Multi White	079148	
4. SHORELINE (On Table)	2¼ in wide	
F841 Sapphire/White	472072	
5. ROSY SWAG (In Urn)	4¼ in wide	
F627 Sapphire Multi White	355137	
6. OLIVE (On Table)	4¼ in wide	
P897 Sapphire/Moss/White	063088	

Shown at bottom, from left to right:

1. ROSY SWAG (In Cabinet)	4¼ in wide	
F627 Rose Multi White	355144	
2. HAREBELL (In Soap Dish)	2¼ in wide	
L631 Rose/Moss/White	056080	
3. OLIVE (In Cabinet)	4¼ in wide	
P897 Rose/Moss/White	063080	
4. RIBBONS (On Extension)	4¼ in wide	
K348 Rose	684114	
5. POLKA (On Extension)	2¼ in wide	
F46 Rose/Sky Blue/White	079457	
6. PRIORY (In Cabinet)	2¼ in wide	
K282 Crushed Strawberry Multi White	533426	
7. LOUISE (On Wall)	4¼ in wide	
K305 Rose Multi White	537144	

Further highlights of our new Wallpaper Borders may be seen on our front and back covers. Designed specifically to co-ordinate with our new fruits stories. For example, from right to left on the front cover:

1. Orchards	4¼ in wide	
K347 Multi Grey	536392	
2. Blueberry	4¼ in wide	
K328 Crushed Strawberry Multi Duck Egg	539953	
3. Orchards	4¼ in wide	
K347 Multi Duck Egg	536983	

For further information, please call toll free 1-800-367-2000.

PUBLICATIONS
LAURA ASHLEY STYLE

Laura Ashley Style by Iain Gale and Susan Irvine is a lavishly illustrated book that explores the various decorative designs of the past that have helped mold the distinctive Laura Ashley image. Superb photography of room schemes shows how Laura Ashley has creatively interpreted these styles today, and will provide a source of inspiration to the endless possibilities of design and decoration.

	Code	Price
Laura Ashley Style	880 275999	$30.00

LAURA ASHLEY BEDROOMS

Laura Ashley Bedrooms by Susan Irvine provides a fascinating guide to the possibilities of bedroom style today whether your ideal is the fantastic opulence of the boudoirs of Versailles or the rustic simplicity of a cottage interior. Beautiful colour photography will inspire you to create a bedroom that expresses your own personal style.

	Code	Price
Laura Ashley Bedrooms	880 282999	$20.00

To order, call toll free 24 hours a day 1-800-367-2000.

SENTRY DUTY
SCARLET

This cheerful corner in a child's bedroom reveals the occupant's passion for toy soldiers. Lining the shelves, the brightly painted wooden guardsmen stand at attention as a gleaming scarlet truck awaits to transport them all away from their post.

Inspired by this passion, the Sentry Duty print is the perfect choice for wallcovering, curtains and vinyl border. We also suggest creating your own cushion covers, tablerounds and other nursery accessories from this and other co-ordinating fabrics or select from our custom made to order program.

The wallcovering, in bright scarlet on a sapphire dotted ground adds to the atmosphere of playfullness with its squadron of tiny soldiers silently marching in formation. This theme is further enhanced by the curtains made of country furnishing cotton in the same print.

On a larger scale, these soldiers march along an eye-catching vinyl border. A smart and practical answer for both Mother and Child.

To order, call toll free, 24 hours a day
1-800-367-2000.

CHECKERS
ROSE

This Mother and Child nursery features Checkers, a wonderful plaid fabric that combines the soft pastels of rose, sapphire and jade. The large curtains in crisp plaid Checkers are drawn back to reveal an alcove devoted to sleep.

A sickle moon looks down upon a Victorian crib that is outfitted with a softly frilled crib bumper, comforter and dust ruffle. The vinyl wallcovering in Candida sapphire stripe, creates a mood of restful calm.

Cushions, toys and a host of useful accessories in the Checkers print add a homey sense of comfort. The slipper chair upholstered in sapphire Hopscotch adds another dimension to the check story—a story smart enough to take a child into young adulthood.